THE ADVENTURES OF TOM SAWYER

by
Mark Twain

Student Packet

Written by
Gloria Levine, M.A.

Contains masters for:

2	Prereading Activities
7	Vocabulary Activities
1	Study Guide
3	Critical Thinking Activities
1	Video Review Activity
3	Literary Analysis Activities
1	Crossword Puzzle
3	Writing Activities
2	Comprehension Quizzes (Average and Advanced)
2	Unit Exams (Average and Advanced)
PLUS	Detailed Answer Key

Note

The text used to prepare this guide was the Signet Classic softcover published by the Penguin Group. The novel was first published in 1876. The page references may differ in other editions.

Please note: Please assess the appropriateness of this book for the age level and maturity of your students prior to reading and discussing it with your class.

ISBN 1-56137-528-4

To order, contact your local school supply store, or—

Novel Units, Inc.
P.O. Box 97
Bulverde, TX 78163-0097

Web site: www.educyberstor.com

Name_____

Directions: Rate each of the following statements before you read the novel. Compare your ratings with a partner's, and discuss why you chose the particular ratings you did. (After you have completed the novel, rate the statements again and discuss whether the novel changed your mind about certain statements.)

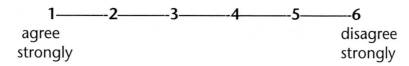

1————2————3————4————5————6
agree   disagree
strongly   strongly

		Before	After
1.	Superstitious beliefs are often based somewhat on fact.	____	____
2.	Parents/guardians usually know what is best for their kids.	____	____
3.	Spare the rod and spoil the child.	____	____
4.	You should try to forgive and forget.	____	____
5.	Revenge is sweet.	____	____
6.	It is wrong to lie.	____	____
7.	Most grown-ups have forgotten what it is like to be a child.	____	____
8.	You should take care of yourself, first.	____	____
9.	Parents need to be strict with kids if they really love them.	____	____
10.	Older children who daydream or enjoy fantasy play are generally lonely or unhappy.	____	____
11.	Sometimes you have to break a promise in order to do the right thing.	____	____
12.	You should never break a promise.	____	____
13.	If you're jealous of someone, the best idea is to make that person jealous.	____	____
14.	If you really care about someone, you would "take the rap" for that person to keep him or her from getting in trouble.	____	____
15.	Once someone pays you for doing what you like to do, it becomes work.	____	____

Name_____

Directions: Each question below is followed by four choices. Before reading the story, circle the choice that BEST tells what YOU would do (or fill in your own response as choice "e." (There is no "right" or "wrong" answer.) After reading the story, answer the questions as Tom and Huck would.

1. Suppose you are being punished because you went over to a friend's house without telling your parents. What would you do if you were told to mow the lawn?
   a) mow the lawn
   b) get your friends to do it
   c) pay someone else to do it
   d) don't mow the lawn
   e) _____

2. Suppose you witness a shooting. If you don't tell what you saw, the wrong person will go to jail—but if you tell, you'll be worried about your own safety. What would you do?
   a) tell in court what you saw
   b) tell the authorities what you saw, but refuse to appear in court
   c) pretend you never saw anything
   d) wait and see if the wrong person is convicted before deciding what to do
   e) _____

3. Suppose a certain girl or boy that you like starts flirting with someone else right in front of you—just to make you jealous. What would you do?
   a) confront the person and say that you don't like what he or she is doing
   b) don't act jealous; just say hello and go somewhere else
   c) pretend you don't see the person and stay where you are
   d) try to make the girl or boy jealous by flirting with someone else
   e) _____

4. Suppose that you and someone you really like were the only ones in the classroom when the other person accidentally knocked over your teacher's favorite vase. What would you do if the teacher came in and angrily asked each of you who had broken the vase?
   a) say that you did it
   b) admit that the other person did it
   c) say that someone else did it
   d) say that you didn't see what happened
   e) _____

Name_____

Directions: Write a brief answer to each study question as you read the novel at home or in class. Use the questions for review before group discussions and before your final exam.

Chapter 1:
1. What has Tom done to make Aunt Polly mad, at the beginning of the story?
2. What is Aunt Polly like? Is she like the "wicked stepmother" you find in fairy tales?
3. Who are Sid and Mary?
4. When Aunt Polly tries to get Tom to admit that he has been playing hooky, she feels his shirt. "But in spite of her Tom knew where the wind lay now." (p. 13) What does that mean?

Chapter 2:
1. What punishment does Aunt Polly think up for Tom? Why is he being punished? Do you think he deserves punishment?
2. Tom tells Jim that Aunt Polly "talks awful, but talk don't hurt—anyways, it don't if she don't cry." What does he mean? What does this show you about him?
3. Reread the description on page 19 of how Tom convinces Jim to give up the pail in exchange for a "white alley." What is a white alley? Why does Jim end up flying down the street with his pail?
4. How does Tom avoid whitewashing the fence?

Chapter 3:
1. Joe Harper and Tom play in the public square. How?
2. Who is Amy Lawrence and why has Tom forgotten her?
3. How is Tom wrongly punished for something Sid did? Why doesn't Aunt Polly admit her mistake? Is she too proud?
4. Why does Tom imagine himself drowned (p. 27)?

Chapter 4:
1. How is Tom at memorizing verses? Why?
2. What does Mary give Tom as a present? Why?
3. What are the tickets for, and why does Tom want the prize?
4. How does Tom embarrass himself at Sunday School in front of Becky?

Chapter 5:
1. How does Tom keep himself entertained during the church service?
2. What happens to Tom's pinch-bug?

Chapter 6:
1. How does Tom try to get out of going to school?
2. Why is Tom the envy of every boy he meets at school on Monday?
3. Who is Huck Finn and how do people feel about him?
4. What plan do Huck and Tom make for getting rid of their warts?
5. Why does Tom admit to the schoolmaster that he is late because he has been talking to Huck?
6. How does Tom let Becky know that he likes her?

Chapter 7:
1. What does Tom tell Becky he plans to be when he grows up?
2. Why does Becky get so angry at Tom after he suggests that they get "engaged"?
3. What is the "chiefest jewel" (p. 58) that Tom tries to give to Becky? What does she do with it?

Chapter 8:
1. After his argument with Becky, Tom comes up with a plan for a new "career." What will he be?
2. How can you tell that Tom is superstitious?
3. What plans does Tom make for running away?

Chapter 9:
1. Where does Tom meet Huck that night? Why?
2. Who do the boys see in the graveyard? What are they doing?
3. Why do Injun Joe and the doctor fight?
4. How is the doctor killed? Why does Muff Potter think he did it?

Chapter 10:
1. What blood pact do Huck and Tom make? Why?
2. As the boys make their pact in the old tannery, somebody sneaks in. Who?
3. Why are the boys so upset by the dog?
4. How does Aunt Polly know that Tom has been out that night?
5. At school the next day, why is Tom flogged?
6. Sitting at his desk, Tom finds his elbow resting on the andiron knob. Why is that "the final feather that broke the camel's back" (p.77)?

Chapter 11:
1. When the body is found, why does everyone think Muff Potter is the murderer?
2. Why does Muff Potter return to the scene of the crime?
3. When Injun Joe lies about the killing, why don't the boys tell everyone the truth?
4. Why does Tom pretend he has a toothache after the murder?
5. Why does Tom go to the jail?

Chapter 12:
1. Becky stops coming to school. How can you tell from Tom's reaction that he is melodramatic—given to exaggeration?
2. What is Aunt Polly's favorite hobby?
3. What happens to Peter, the cat?
4. Becky returns to school. Is she still angry with Tom?

Chapter 13:
1. Why does Tom make up his mind to run away?
2. Why is Joe also planning to run away?
3. What do the boys take along when they run away?
4. Where do the boys go when they run away? How do they get there?
5. As the boys fall asleep, they start feeling guilty. About what?

Chapter 14:
1. How do the boys pass the time on the island?
2. Why are the cannons being fired?
3. Who gets homesick?
4. Why do you think Tom wrote on the bark and put his treasures in Joe's hat?

Chapter 15:
1. How does Tom get home? Why does he go?
2. What does Tom overhear when he gets home?
3. What does Tom do after Aunt Polly falls asleep?
4. How does Tom get back to the island? How do the boys react to his return?

Chapter 16:
1. What new activities do the boys come up with?
2. How does Tom keep the homesick boys from going home?
3. What does Huck teach the other boys to do?
4. Why do Joe and Tom say that they have to search for Joe's knife—and then disappear?
5. What do the boys find when they return to their "camp" after the storm?
6. Why do the boys smoke a "peace pipe"? Why does it make them so happy?

Chapter 17:
1. How do the people of St. Petersburg seem to feel about the boys' absence? Why do they think the boys are dead?
2. What is the funeral service like?
3. When do the boys return? How are they treated?

Chapter 18:
1. How does Tom convince Aunt Polly that dreams can hold the truth?
2. How do most of the kids at school treat Tom after his return from the island?
3. How do Tom and Becky try to make each other jealous. Do they succeed?
4. Why does Alfred want to get Tom into trouble? How does he manage that?

Chapter 19:
1. Why is Aunt Polly so angry with Tom after she talks with Sereny Harper about Tom's dream?
2. Why is Aunt Polly so happy after checking Tom's jacket pocket?

Chapter 20:
1. Why does Tom get whipped by Mr. Dobbins? Who could have prevented the whipping?
2. Why does Becky almost get in trouble with Mr. Dobbins? How does she stay out of trouble?
3. Is Becky still angry with Tom? Is Tom still angry with Becky?
4. Why is Tom plotting vengeance against Alfred? What sort of revenge do you suppose he is planning?

Chapter 21:
1. Why does the schoolmaster get more and more tyrannical as vacation approaches?
2. Why does the painter's son hate the schoolmaster even more than most?
3. What sorts of exercises do the students perform on "Examination Day"?
4. How do the students get revenge against their teacher?

Chapter 22:
1. Why is Tom angry with Judge Frazer for dying when he does?
2. What are some of the high points of the vacation?
3. What are some of the low points of the vacation?
4. Explain the last line describing Joe and Huck at the end of the chapter, "Poor fellows, they, like Tom, had suffered a relapse."

Chapter 23:
1. At the end of the second day of the trial, "Tom was out late that night and came to bed through the window. He was in a tremendous state of excitement." (p. 148) Why?
2. Why doesn't Potter's lawyer cross-examine any of the witnesses who give damaging testimony against Potter?
3. What does Tom say in court?
4. What happens to Injun Joe?

Chapter 24:
1. Why is Tom having nightmares?
2. Why is Huck's "confidence in the human race well-nigh obliterated" (p. 151)?

Chapter 25:
1. Why do Tom and Huck start digging under various old trees?
2. What does each boy plan to do with any treasure the boys find?
3. Where else do the boys plan to look for treasure?

Chapter 26:
1. Why do the boys decide to wait until Saturday to enter the "haunted house"? How do they spend Friday?
2. Who else enters the "haunted house"?
3. What plans do the boys overhear the robbers make?
4. Why does Injun Joe dig in the corner of the house? What does he find?
5. How does Injun Joe figure out that someone else has been in the house? Why doesn't he look upstairs?

Chapter 27:
1. Why does Tom go to the two taverns in town?   What important information does he learn?
2. How do the boys plan to get into "number two"?

Chapter 28:
1. Where does Huck sleep most nights?
2. What does Tom discover is stored in the "haunted room" of the "Temperance Tavern." Why is this ironic? (Why isn't this what you would expect?)
3. After Tom gets into the tavern room and sees Injun Joe, what do he and Huck agree to do to get the money box?

Chapter 29:
1. What sort of party do Becky's parents have for her?
2. What does Tom convince Becky to do that night?
3. What does Huck find out about the robbers while Tom is off at the picnic?
4. Why does Huck want to help the widow? To whom does he go for help?

Chapter 30:
1. Why doesn't Huck tell the Welshman the truth about the "Spaniard" at first? How does the Welshman figure out that Huck is holding back?
2. Why doesn't the Welshman tell the widow at first that it is Huck she should be thanking?
3. How long does it take Aunt Polly and Becky's mother to worry about the absence of Becky and Tom? Why does it take so long?
4. Why does the Widow Douglas come to the Welshman's home to take care of Huck?

Chapter 31:
1. Why does Tom blow out Becky's candle as they wander through the caves, lost?
2. After they find a spring, Tom suggests they go no farther. Why?
3. What do Tom and Becky have to eat?
4. Why does Tom decide to explore some side passages near the spring? How does he plan to find his way back to the spring?
5. How do Tom and Injun Joe meet in the cave? What happens next?

Chapter 32:
1. How do Tom and Becky get out of the cave?
2. Why doesn't Tom tell Huck about his adventure in the cave right away?
3. What happens to Injun Joe's partner?
4. Why is Tom so shocked to hear the judge say that the cave has been triple locked?

Chapter 33:
1. How did Injun Joe die?
2. According to the narrator, what still attracts tourists' attention at McDougal's cave—years after Injun Joe's death?
3. What sort of petition had been on its way to the governor? How does the narrator seem to feel about the idea of pardoning someone like Injun Joe?
4. How does Tom figure out where the money is?
5. How do Tom and Huck get into the cave?
6. Why does Huck want to leave the money in the cave? How does Tom convince him otherwise?
7. How do the boys get the bags of money to the Widow Douglas's house?
8. Who is waiting for the boys at the widow's house? Why?

Chapter 34:
1. Why does Huck want to "slope"? (p. 211)
2. Why does Tom cuff Sid's ears? What secret did Sid tell?
3. What plans does the widow have for Huck? How does he probably feel when he hears about those plans?
4. How does everyone find out about the money Tom and Huck found? How much is there?

Chapter 35:
1. Are Huck and Tom allowed to keep the money?
2. Why does Judge Thatcher compare Tom Sawyer to George Washington? (p. 215)
3. What plans does Judge Thatcher have for Tom's future? How do you suppose Tom feels about that?
4. Why does Huck run away from the widow?
5. How does Tom convince Huck to return to the widow and to school?
6. How do you picture Tom and Huck ten years later?

glowering 16	derision 17	ambuscade 17	delectable 15
insignificant 18	skylarking 18	expeditions 19	slackened 20
surveyed 20	alacrity 21	decanter 22	covet 22
intrepid 23	diluted 23	aides-de-campe 24	furtive 25
exultation 26	potent 26	desolate 27	stealthy 28
deluge 28	martyr 28	blighted 28	grandeur 30
disconcerted 30	edifice 31	waylaid 32	reprimand 32
mien 33	majestic 35	prodigy 35	guileful 36

Directions: An analogy is a comparison. Here are two examples:

NO is to YES as OFF is to ON.

HILL is to MOUNTAIN as STREAM is to RIVER

Use words from the vocabulary list to complete the analogies, below. Then create analogies for five more of the vocabulary words and give them to a partner to complete.

1. PLAN is to PLOT as ATTACK is to _____.

2. WISE is to OWL as _____ is to FOX.

3. TWISTING is to SNAKING as FROLICKING is to _____.

4. BEAMING is to PROUD as _____ is to ANGRY.

5. BEARING is to DEMEANOR as _____ is to APPEARANCE.

6. BLAZE is to TRAIL as BUILD is to _____.

7. PACIFIED is to SOOTHED   as RUFFLED is to _____.

8. DENNIS is to MENACE as EINSTEIN is to _____.

9. ATTENDANTS are to QUEENS as _____ are to GENERALS.

10. RELUCTANCE is to "Do I have to?" as _____ is to "Right away, sir!"

Name_____

seductive 38	hospitable 38	vestibule 38	gantlet 38 (gauntlet)
laggards 39	restive 40	millenium 41	vagrant 41
discourse 42	facetious 42	odious 43	mortified 45
adherent 46	disdain 46	pariah 46	hogsheads 46
hove 49	manifest 51	noncomittal 51	portentous 52
juncture 52	ostentation 53	repulsed 58	andiron 59
zephyr 60	constrained 61	insensibly 61	grisly 61
zenith 61	incantation 62	pettishly 62	cogitating 62

Directions: Divide the words above among the members of your group or class. Turn to the pages on which your words appear in the novel. After examining how each word is used in context, complete a word map for it, using the format below. (You'll need extra paper to make more maps.) Explain your finished maps to classmates.

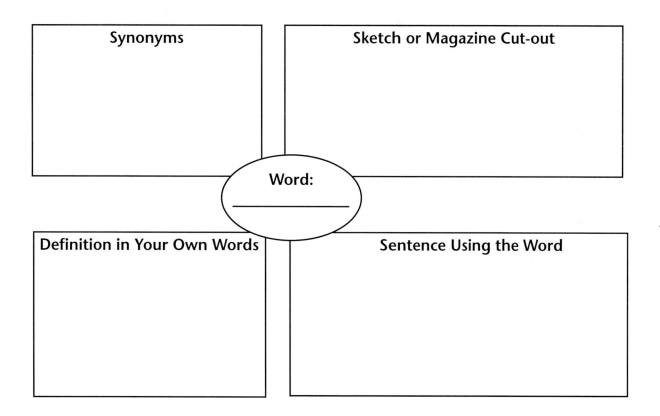

© Novel Units, Inc.

Name_____

combatants 69	inarticulately 69	tannery 71	mum 72
fetters 74	persecuted 76	impudence 79	serene 79
miscreant 80	dejected 84	havoc 85	remorse 86
compact 89	dauntless 92	lugubrious 74	quailed 75

Directions: Add one of the words in the vocabulary list to each "synonym train" below.

1. depressed—despondent—joyless—_____

2. calm—collected—composed—_____

3. agreement—contract—pact—_____

4. guilt—penitence—regret—_____

5. chaos—damage—destruction—_____

6. bonds—chains—manacles—_____

7. back talk—lip—rudeness—_____

8. mistreated—victimized—wronged—_____

9. audacious—bold—brave—_____

10. villain—vicious person—demon—_____

Make additional synonym trains for the words you have not yet used.

11. _____—_____—_____—_____

12. _____—_____—_____—_____

13. _____—_____—_____—_____

14. _____—_____—_____—_____

15. _____—_____—_____—_____

16. _____—_____—_____—_____

credulous 96	fruitless 103	sumptuous 105	charily 109
abashed 117	repentant 120	swarthy 122	sham 123
vindictive 124	jubilant 124	assent 125	artlessly 125

Directions: Match each word or phrase below with the word in the **antonym** list above that means the <u>opposite</u>.

1. _____ unremorseful

2. _____ disagreement

3. _____ boldly

4. _____ skeptical

5. _____ unembarrassed

6. _____ depressed

7. _____ fair-skinned

8. _____ forgiving

9. _____ guilefully

10. _____ meager

11. _____ productive

12. _____ genuine

lethargy 132	retribution 135	dominie 135	festoons 136
gesticulation 136	edification 137	unpalatable 137	pate 141
convalescent 142	phrenologist 143	forbearance 144	counsel 148
diffident 150	fickle 151	omniscient 152	sepulchral 157
athwart 161	infernal 163		

Directions: Complete each sentence with a word from the list.

1. Hold your head high and speak up confidently! Don't be _____.

2. The weather has been _____—balmy one minute, stormy the next.

3. She couldn't hear what he was saying, but she could tell by his frantic _____ that something was wrong.

4. He was going to defend himself, but the judge suggested that he hire _____.

5. The _____ tones of the wolf's howl frightened the young campers.

6. The minister offered his sermons for the _____ of his listeners.

7. He is better now but he is still _____ so I think I'll wait awhile to visit him.

8. He told the barber to leave one long strand of hair to comb across his bald _____.

9. After examining the shape of the woman's skull, the _____ analyzed her character traits

10. An _____ narrator seems to know everything about what a character does, thinks, and feels.

Write sentences for the words you have not yet used.

Name_____

Directions: Form a group of three and figure out the mystery words together.

Step 1: Each member of the group picks a card from the same set and reads the clue on it to the others in the group.

Step 2: Members help each other figure out the mystery word for that set of clues. (Take a look at the vocabulary box only if you are stumped.)

Set #1:

This three-syllable word is a noun.	In classical mythology, a vast maze built to house the Minotaur.	an intricate combination of passages in which it is difficult to find one's way

Set #2:

This person is no relation to 007.	a hobo or loafer	from the Latin word, "vagari"—to wander

Set #3:

An antonym for this word is "blushed."	This is related to the French word for "white."	made pale by sickness or fear

Make your own clue cards for the group on the back of your paper. Choose words from the vocabulary box.

attrition 168	gunwale 168	auspicious 171	secondary 174	labyrinth 176
elude 177	daubed 177	wake 177	communing 178	agues 178
stile 178	stalwart 180	vagabond 181	brace 181	blanched 184
jaded 185	self-possession 185	belittled 186	countenance 187	ransacked 188

Directions: One partner draws a dotted line around two words in each group that are opposite in meaning. The other partner draws a solid line around the two words in each group that are similar in meaning. Partners are welcome to help each other and encouraged to discuss their answers.

1. apathy   windfall   serendipity
   spasm   refugee   enthusiasm

2. unkempt   conspicuous   magnanimous
   unanimous   subtle   benevolent

3. gratification   laudation   provision
   moiety   half   displeasure

4. recess   projection   stupor
   shackle   foundry   bond

5. gloated   whetted   sharpened
   routed   dissented   agreed

6. crimson   insipid   exciting
   delirious   hideous   red

7. avocation   profession   vestibule
   laudation   chasm   criticism

8. sinuous   unavailing   oppressive
   melancholy   meandering   effective

9. provisions   huzzas   supplies
   stalactites   pallets   boos

10. pitfall   snare   animation
    lethargy   slope   auditory

Name_____

Directions: The report card below is different from the one that Mr. Dobbins probably gave Tom. Think of the Tom that you know from reading the story and pretend that YOU are his teacher. Give him a grade in each subject (A, B, C, D, or F). Give him an S (satisfactory) or U (unsatisfactory) for Work Habits and Social Skills. In the "Comments" section, explain why you gave him the grade you did.

St. Petersburg School
Report to Parents on Student Progress

Student Name _____ Grade _____
School Year: 1841
Teacher: _____

Attendance Record:

	Sept.	Oct.	Nov.	Dec.	Jan.	Feb.	Mar.	Apr.	May	June	TOTAL
absent											
present											
tardy											

A= Outstanding   B=Excellent   C=Average   D=Needs Improvement   F=Failing

Subject	Grade	Comments
Reading		
Arithmetic		
Spelling		
Science		
History		
Handwriting		
Geography		
Work Habits and Social Skills Works neatly		
Pays attention in class		
Follows oral and written directions		
Exercises self-control		

Directions: *The Adventures of Tom Sawyer* has been censored in some school districts—mostly because of its portrayal of African Americans and Native Americans. Below are some passages from the book. Some readers agree they reflect prejudiced attitudes, but **belong** in the book because they help paint a picture of the way things were during the 1830's. Place a **B** by the passage if this is your opinion. Other readers think that certain passages are racist, objectionable, and should be **CUT**. Place an **X** by the passage if you agree with this view. Still others don't find some of the passages racist or objectionable. Place an **O** by the passage if this is your **opinion**. Be ready to discuss your answers.

1._____ [when Tom tries to convince Jim to do some of the whitewashing while Tom fetches water]: "Can't, Mars Tom. Ole missis she tole me I got to go an' git dis water an' not stop foolin' roun' wid anybody. She say she spec' Mars Tom gwyne to ax me to whitewash, an' so she tole me go 'long an' 'tend to my own business..." (p. 18)

2._____ [Tom expresses his cynicism about Huck's belief in a wart-removal cure passed by word of mouth.] "Well, what of it? They'll all lie. Leastaways all but the nigger, I don't know *him.* But I never see a nigger that *wouldn't* lie. Shucks! Now you tell me how Bob Tanner done it, Huck." (p. 47)

3._____ Huck "admits" to Tom that he sometimes sits down and eats alongside of blacks—but that he isn't proud of it.

4._____ The author explains Tom's reference to the dog's bark by saying that one describes a slave-owner's dog differently from his slave. "If Mr. Harbison had owned a slave named Bull, Tom would have spoken of him as "Harbison's Bull'; but a son or a dog of that name was "Bull Harbison'." (p. 74).

5._____ [The Welshman talks to Huck about the threats Huck has overheard "Injun Joe" make.] "It's all plain enough now. When you talked about notching ears and slitting noses, I judged that this was your own embellishment, because white men don't take that sort of revenge. But an Injun! That's a different matter, altogether." (p. 184)

Should this book be banned? Give at least three reasons for your answer on the back of your paper. Then defend your answer in a classroom debate.

Name_____

Directions: The pie below represents a typical day for Tom. Each of the four slices represents six hours. Estimate how much time he spends each day on SLEEP, SCHOOL, BIBLE STUDY, GIRLS, CHORES, FANTASY PLAY, EXPLORING, MISCELLANEOUS. Further divide the pie into different-sized slices to represent proportionately how Tom spends 24 hours in one day, and label each slice.

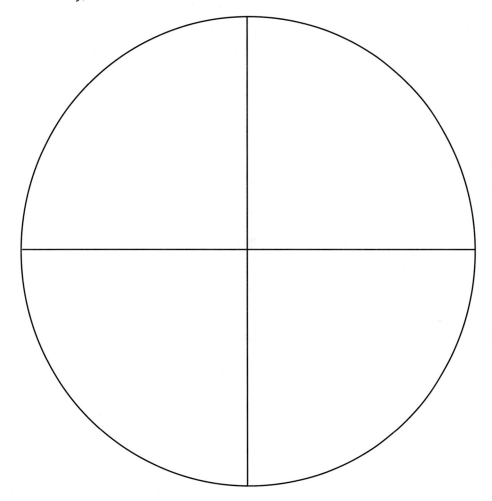

Pretend that you are Tom. Think about how you would change the size of some of the slices, if you had a choice. Write the conversation that you (as Tom) have with Huck about how you would spend your time if it weren't for grown-ups.

Now create another "pie" on the back of this sheet. Show how YOU spend a typical day. How would you change the size of some of your slices if you could?

Name_____

Directions: Tom had to decide whether or not to testify at Muff Potter's trial that he had seen Injun Joe kill Doc Robinson. Help him weigh the pros and cons of testifying.

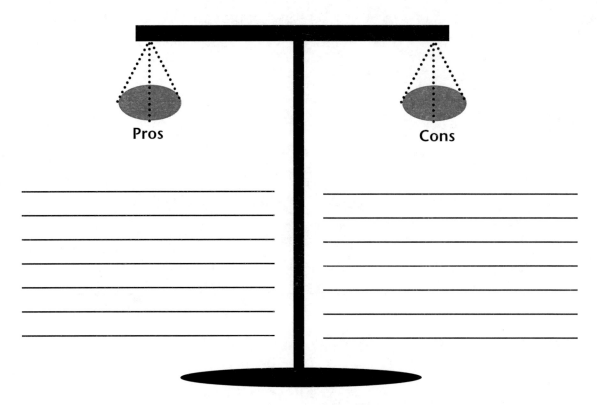

Pros   Cons

Now list two other options he had, summarizing the pros and cons:

option	pros and cons
1.	
2.	

Write an essay explaining why he reached the decision he did and why it was (or was not) the best decision, in your opinion.

Similes

A <u>simile</u> is a comparison using "like" or "as".

| | Her hands are **like** ice cubes. |
| **or** | Her hands are **as** cold **as** ice. |

<u>For</u> <u>each</u> <u>of</u> <u>the</u> <u>similes</u> <u>below,</u> <u>tell</u>
      a) what two things are compared
      b) how they are alike
      c) another comparison the author might have used

1.   (As Tom and the new boy fought they were) "gripped together like cats." (p. 17)
      a)
      b)
      c)

2.   (The thought of the other boys having fun while he painted the fence) "burnt him like fire" (p. 19)
      a)
      b)
      c)

3.   (As Tom threw clods at Sid, the clods) "raged around Sid like a hailstorm" (p. 24)
      a)
      b)
      c)

4.   "The mighty river lay like an ocean at rest." (p. 89)
      a)
      b)
      c)

5.   (While spying on Injun Joe) "there was a season of waiting anxiety that weighed upon Huck's spirits like a mountain." (p. 171)
      a)
      b)
      c)

Directions: View a video adaptation of the novel. Write a review of the film. In your review, mention changes that were made in the book and tell whether you thought those changes, additions, and deletions benefited the story. Give your opinion of other aspects of the film, such as the casting and filming.

Below is a chart you might use organize your ideas before writing.

In the book...	but in the movie...
opening scene:	opening scene:
main events:	main events:
final scene:	final scene:
characters as imagined:	characters as cast:

Name_____

The Adventures of Tom Sawyer
Activity #16: **Literary Analysis: Diction and Dialect**
Use After Reading
Note: This activity has two pages.

Diction and Dialect

I. Diction refers to the words an author chooses. Mark Twain often used "big" literary words when he could have used more conversational words or even slang. Reread the passage below that describes how Tom feels after he is wrongly punished for breaking the sugar bowl.

...He wandered far away from the accustomed haunts of boys and sought desolate places that were in harmony with his spirit. A log raft in the river invited him, and he seated himself on its outer edge, and contemplated the dreary vastness of the stream, wishing the while that he could only be drowned all at once and unconsciously, without undergoing the uncomfortable routine devised by nature. Then he thought of his flower. He got it out, rumpled and wilted, and it mightily increased his dismal felicity...(p. 27)

A. Find several synonyms for these words:
accustomed _____
desolate _____
contemplated _____
felicity _____

B. Rewrite the paragraph using more conversational words. (Use separate paper or the back of this sheet.)

C. Rewrite the paragraph using colloquial and slang terms.

II. Dialect. While Mark Twain often used literary words, he also broke away from the style of writers of his time by writing <u>American</u> <u>colloquial</u> <u>speech</u>. His characters often speak in <u>dialect</u>. Their pronunciation and even the words they use often differ from those of speakers who aren't from their region.

A. Make a list of words in the book that are pronounced in a way that is different from the "standard." For example
1. "jest" for "just"
2.
3.
4.
5.

B. Make a list of words and phrases that seem to be unique to Tom and Huck's time or region. Use context as your guide in defining these vocabulary terms. For example,
1. "cipher" for "write"
2.
3.
4.
5.

C. Below are some colloquial expressions which appear on just one page (page 12). Explain what they mean, and add others from the novel to the list :

1. "Can't learn an old dog new tricks."

2. "…I get my dander up."

3. "He's full of the Old Scratch."

4. "Spare the rod and spile the child."

5.

6.

7.

8.

9.

10.

11.

12.

Directions: Talk with other members of your group about what an adventure is. What adventures did Tom and his friends have? Which were real? Which were imaginary? Which ones involved keeping secrets from adults?

Now think about adventures that you have had with your best friends. Did any involve running away from home or going to a secret place? Which ones will you remember forever, and why? In the space below and on the back of your paper, describe one of the most memorable adventures you have had with friends. Display your group's essays on a bulletin board entitled "Beyond the Adventures of Tom Sawyer."

Name_____

ACROSS

3. a dead one was part of a wart cure
4. The Widow _____ adopted Huck.
5. Tom gave one of these to Becky.
7. Huck Finn, a.k.a "Finn the Red-____"
10. Aunt Polly dosed Tom with Pain-_____.
11. The boys heard these being fired.
13. Huck's usual place for sleeping.
15. Tom was supposed to paint this.
17. Alfred spilled ink on Tom's _____book.
19. He was angry—he didn't drink the cream.
20. The boys' password.
22. Tom lived in St. _____, Missouri.
25. Becky gave one of these to Tom.
27. Tom, Huck, and Joe pretended to be these.
30. Tom had to spend part of the summer in bed due to this.
32. Muff Potter was accused of the murder because his ____ was found by the body.
33. Tom, Huck, and Joe enjoyed eating the eggs of this animal while on the island.

DOWN

1. His mother was Aunt Polly's sister.
2. The boys ran off to _____ Island.
3. Tom and Becky were lost in this.
6. Sid was the one who broke this bowl.
8. Ben gave Tom this for the honor of painting.
9. Everyone thought he was Doc's murderer.
12. Tom tried to give Becky an _____ knob.
14. the town where Mark Twain grew up
15. Tom trapped this while sitting in church.
16. what Tom told Becky he wanted to be one day
18. Huck taught Tom and Joe to smoke this.
21. Becky was impressed by Tom's ability at this.
23. Aunt Polly commonly punished Tom by hitting his head with this.
24. He wanted Hoss Williams' body.
25. Aunt Polly's cat
26. Tom gave Becky one of these fruits.
28. When they had only one left, they stayed at the spring.
29. A cemetery was part of the cure for these.
31. the vehicle the boys used to get to the island

Name_____

Directions: Label each statement T for True or F for False. Change the false statements into true ones on the other side of your paper.

__ 1. Tom fought with the well-dressed boy because the boy insulted Tom's Aunt Polly.

__ 2. Tom's Aunt Polly treated him cruelly and he hated her for it.

__ 3. Aunt Polly told Tom to wash the fence as punishment for fighting with Sid.

__ 4. Tom got other boys to whitewash the fence by giving them a tin soldier, a key, and other treasures.

__ 5. Joe Harper and Tom were good friends and liked to pretend that they were generals of opposing armies.

__ 6. Tom "forgot" his girlfriend Amy Lawrence when he met Becky Thatcher.

__ 7. Aunt Polly punished Tom for breaking the sugar bowl, but Sid was the one who did it.

__ 8. Tom memorized dozens of verses to earn a Bible.

__ 9. A dog went wild in church because it had been pinched by Tom's pinchbug.

__10. Tom pulled his tooth out with a pliers so that he could spit better.

__11. Most of the mothers felt sorry for Huck and tried to make him feel loved and wanted.

__12. Huck and Tom went to the graveyard late at night to see if they could steal the gold teeth from the body of a man who had just been buried.

__13. Tom gave Becky a peach and revealed that he loved her.

__14. Tom told Becky he planned to be a circus clown when he grew up.

__15. Becky got angry with Tom because she thought that an andiron was a stupid present to give someone you want to marry.

__16. Tom was superstitious.

__17. Muff Potter and Injun Joe killed the doctor together.

__18. Huck and Tom made a blood pact not to tell that they knew who killed Doc Robinson.

__19. After the murder, Tom bound his mouth shut at night so that he wouldn't say something about the murder in his sleep.

__20. Aunt Polly didn't believe in new-fangled medicines.

Name_____

Directions: Fill in each blank with a word, name, or phrase.

When Tom Sawyer 1._____, Aunt Polly decided to punish him by having him 2._____ the fence. Tom got out of that job by 3._____. One Sunday, he traded the treasures he collected during the fence caper for twenty-eight 4._____ that other children had earned by 5._____. The Superintendent doubted that Tom deserved the prize, a 6._____, and his suspicions were confirmed when Thomas could not recite the names of the first two 7._____. The next day, Tom tried to get out of going to school, but Aunt Polly took care of the problem by 8._____ and sent him off to class. Huck Finn showed Tom a dead 9._____ he had found, and told Tom that it would be useful for curing 10._____. According to Huck, all they had to do was throw it at a 11._____ who had come after the body of someone 12._____ and say a magic spell. The boys agreed to go to the 13._____ at 14._____. Tom was late to class, but didn't mind being punished because he knew that the teacher would make him sit 15._____. He gave the new girl, 16._____, a peach and made her some 17._____ on his slate. Then he wrote the words, "18._____." She was pleased when he told her about being engaged, until he happened to mention 19._____. In a fury, she refused to listen to him any more and struck down the special 20._____ he tried to give her. That night, when Tom met 21._____ as they had agreed, they were surprised to see three men, 22. _____ _____, _____ _____, and Doc Robinson digging up the body that had just been buried. The three men fought, and the boys saw 23._____ _____ kill 24._____ _____. Terrified, they made a blood pact not to 25._____, and they stuck to it even after 26._____ _____ was arrested for the crime. Tom was thrilled when 27._____ returned to school after a long absence. When he found that she was still angry, he decided to escape from his troubles by 28._____ with 29._____ and 30._____.

Identification: Find a character on the right who matches the description on the left. Write the letter of the character next to the matching number. Each character is to be used only once.

___ 1. He wanted to run away from home because his mother punished him for drinking cream he knew nothing about.

___ 2. He finally told the truth about who the murderer was.

___ 3. He enjoyed snitching on Tom to Aunt Polly.

___ 4. The son of a town drunkard, he did as he pleased.

___ 5. He went to trial for a murder he did not commit.

___ 6. She was Tom's love before the new girl moved to town.

___ 7. This old woman never enjoyed punishing Tom, but felt that it was her duty.

___ 8. She announced that she would give Huck a home and an education.

___ 9. Becky made Tom jealous by reading books with this "St. Louis smarty" he had fought earlier.

___ 10. Tom's kind half-sister, she gave him a Barlow knife.

___ 11. He killed Doc Robinson and planned to hurt the widow.

___ 12. Tom was charmed by this new girl with blue eyes and yellow braids.

___ 13. He promised to pay two others to help him steal a body.

A. Aunt Polly
B. Tom Sawyer
C. Huck Finn
D. Joe Harper
E. Injun Joe
F. Doc Robinson
G. Muff Potter
H. Sid
I. Mary
J. Becky Thatcher
K. Amy Lawrence
L. Alfred Temple
M. Widow Douglas

Multiple Choice: To the left of each item number, write the number of the BEST response.

_____ 1. Sid pointed out the color of the thread on Tom's collar so that Aunt Polly would
(1) punish Tom for swimming and playing hooky
(2) punish Tom for ripping his collar while pouring water on his head
(3) be distracted from the sugar bowl Sid had broken
(4) praise Sid for finding the black thread

____ 2. Which of these best describes the way Tom felt about his Aunt Polly?
(1) He was irritated by her and enjoyed making her cry.
(2) He hated her and wished that he had been sent to an orphanage after his mother died.
(3) He didn't care one way or the other about her.
(4) He loved her and knew that he could often get around her by making her laugh.

____ 3. The boys whitewashed the fence for Tom because
(1) he paid them to do it
(2) they wanted to help out their friend so that he would be free to play
(3) he convinced them that whitewashing was fun
(4) he threatened to tell on them if they didn't

____ 4. The main reason Tom traded his treasures for the Sunday School tickets was so that he could
(1) have a Bible of his own
(2) be the center of attention as he got an award
(3) impress Becky by reciting hundreds of verses
(4) avoid the boredom of listening to a boring sermon

____ 5. In the graveyard, Tom and Huck saw
(1) Muff Potter hit Doc Robinson over the head
(2) Doc Robinson threaten Muff Potter
(3) Muff Potter kill Doc Robinson
(4) Injun Joe kill Doc Robinson

____ 6. Becky was angry with Tom for weeks because
(1) he threw away the flower she had given him
(2) he let it slip that he had been engaged to Amy
(3) he wouldn't promise to marry her someday
(4) he had a fistfight with Alfred

____ 7. While everyone was searching for Tom, Huck, and Joe, the boys were
(1) playing and camping on a nearby island
(2) digging for treasure in the haunted house
(3) lost in a cave
(4) playing Robin Hood in a nearby tavern

_____ 8. After running away, the boys put off coming home until they could
(1) get a look at their Missing Persons Posters
(2) sneak into their beds unnoticed
(3) sit in on their own funerals
(4) make sure that they were safe from Injun Joe

_____ 9. Tom was able to describe exactly what Aunt Polly and Joe Harper's mother had said about them while they were away because
(1) Sid told Tom about the conversation
(2) Tom had sneaked home and overheard the conversation
(3) Tom had had a vivid dream about the conversation
(4) he knew both women so well that he had a good idea of what they had probably said

_____ 10. Which of the following was NOT a problem the boys had when they ran away from home?
(1) Injun Joe chased them across the island.
(2) They grew homesick.
(3) A storm drenched their camp.
(4) They felt guilty about stealing food.

_____ 11. Which of the following are NOT people the boys pretended to be?
(1) generals of armies invading the town
(2) Robin Hood and his friends and enemies
(3) Batman and his friends and enemies
(4) pirates

_____ 12. Why did Aunt Polly's cat act so wild?
(1) Huck blew pipe smoke at him.
(2) Injun Joe gave him poison.
(3) Aunt Polly gave him whiskey.
(4) Tom gave him Pain-Killer.

_____ 13. The ink on Tom's spelling book
(1) was accidentally spilled by Tom while he was reaching for Becky's braid
(2) was purposely spilled by Tom so he couldn't do the lesson
(3) was purposely spilled by Alfred to get Tom in trouble
(4) was purposely spilled by Becky to get Tom in trouble

____ 14. Becky ripped Mr. Dobbins's book
      (1) on purpose because she hated the teacher
      (2) on purpose to get Tom in trouble
      (3) by accident when she walked by his desk
      (4) by accident while snooping in his desk

____ 15. When Mr. Dobbins asked who had ripped his book
      (1) Tom said that he had done it
      (2) Alfred said that Tom had done it
      (3) Becky said that Tom had done it
      (4) Becky admitted that she had done it

____ 16. The students got back at their teacher on Examination Day by
      (1) acting up in front of the visitors
      (2) rigging a pot of molasses to fall on his head
      (3) having a cat lift his wig
      (4) putting chalk in the erasers and throwing spitballs

____ 17. When Tom admitted in court that he had seen who killed Doc Robinson,
      (1) Injun Joe dashed out of the courtroom through a window
      (2) Injun Joe grabbed Tom and held a knife to his throat
      (3) Huck vowed he would never speak to Tom again
      (4) Huck stood up and admitted that he too had seen Injun Joe commit the murder

____ 18. The gold treasure in the haunted house was buried there by
      (1) Injun Joe and his partner
      (2) a gang that had used the house sometime before
      (3) Tom and Huck
      (4) the widow's late husband

____ 19. Tom and Huck overheard Injun Joe and his partner talk about
      (1) how they had murdered Hoss Williams
      (2) how they had murdered the widow's late husband
      (3) plans to do a dangerous job and then go to Texas
      (4) plans to kill the boys and then go to California

_____ 20. While Tom and Becky were getting lost in the cave, Huck was busy
     (1) smoking his pipe on the island
     (2) taking reading lessons from Aunt Polly
     (3) searching the cave for them
     (4) foiling Injun Joe's plans to hurt the widow

_____ 21. At the end, Tom figured out that the money was located
     (1) in the tavern
     (2) in the cave
     (3) on the island
     (4) in the church

_____ 22. If the Judge hadn't had the cave locked up,
     (1) the widow wouldn't have adopted Huck
     (2) Becky and Tom would't have gotten lost there
     (3) Injun Joe wouldn't have died there
     (4) Huck and Tom wouldn't have found the treasure

_____ 23. The Widow took care of Huck while he recovered from
     (1) a gunshot wound
     (2) a broken leg
     (3) a fever
     (4) a knife wound

_____ 24. In the end, the money
     (1) was locked forever in the cave
     (2) was never found
     (3) was found by professional treasure-hunters
     (4) was divided between Tom and Huck

_____ 25. Which of the following is most similar to the way Huck felt about being
     adopted by the widow?
     (1) the way a mouse might feel if a cat trapped it in her claws
     (2) how you might feel if your grandmother bought you an ugly jacket
     (3) the way you might feel if your parents won the lottery
     (4) the way a storeowner might feel if a robber stole his money

Writing Response

I. Analysis

Directions: Select A or B and write a one-paragraph answer. Use complete sentences and include at least two clearly explained examples. Indicate the letter of the question you answer.

    A. Tom, Huck, and Joe have several adventures together—some real and some imagined. Describe one real adventure and one fantasy adventure that they have.

    B. Tom and Huck agree never to tell what they have seen in the graveyard. Explain why they make that pact—and why Tom breaks it.

II. Critical and Creative Thinking

    C. You are Becky. Write an entry in your diary the day after the teacher discovers the ripped page in his book. Tell what happened and how you felt about what Tom did.

    D. Imagine the scene at the dinner table the evening after Tom and his friends come home after running away. Write the conversation that Tom has with Aunt Polly, Sid, and Mary.

Directions: Use separate paper for your answers to each of the sections in this test. Be sure to clearly identify your answers by writing the heading (for instance, "II. Short Answer") and the number or letter of each item.

I. Identification: Explain who each character is and briefly describe him or her in one or two sentences.

A. Aunt Polly
B. Tom Sawyer
C. Huck Finn
D. Joe Harper
E. Injun Joe
F. Doc Robinson
G. Muff Potter
H. Sid
I. Mary
J. Becky Thatcher
K. Alfred Temple
L. Widow Douglas

II. Short Answer: Answer each question in one or two complete sentences.

1. At the beginning of the story, how were Aunt Polly's suspicions that Tom had played hooky confirmed?
2. How would you describe Tom's feelings toward his Aunt Polly—and her feelings toward him?
3. How did Tom get out of whitewashing the fence?
4. How did Tom get so many tickets in Sunday School and why did he want them?
5. Why were Tom and Huck in the graveyard at midnight?
6. What did Tom and Huck see in the graveyard?
7. Why did Becky Thatcher get so angry with Tom?
8. Why did the boys disappear and where did they go?
9. What was going on when the boys returned home after running away?
10. Why did Aunt Polly give Tom Pain-Killer and why did she decide he could stop taking it?
11. Describe two times that Tom was punished for something he didn't do, despite his protestations.
12. Describe one time that Tom willingly accepted punishment for something he didn't do.

13. How did the students make their teacher a laughing stock on Examination Day and why did they do it?
14. Why was a search party sent out for Becky and Tom?
15. How did Tom and Huck become rich?
16. Why was Muff Potter accused of Doc Robinson's death?
17. How did everyone learn that Injun Joe had killed the doctor?
18. Why did Injun Joe seek revenge against the doctor and against the widow?
19. How did Injun Joe die?
20. Why did Huck run away from the widow, at the end of the story—and how did Tom convince him to return to her?

III. Analysis
Directions: Select A or B.

A. Mark Twain criticizes several aspects of the society of his day by poking fun at them. Describe one instance of social criticism you found in *The Adventures of Tom Sawyer.*

B. Support or refute (prove wrong) the following statement with at least three examples from the book:
Tom and Huck are the epitome of youthful rebellion and lighthearted independence.

IV. Critical and Creative Thinking
Directions: Select C or D.

C. Write an essay explaining why this novel has been censored by some school systems. Explain how you would defend or criticize a school board's decision to ban this book.

D. Write an interior monologue that reveals Tom Sawyer's thoughts right before he decides to tell Muff Potter's lawyer what he knows about the murder.

Answer Key

Study Questions

Chapter 1: 1-ate some jam 2-Aunt Polly is a religious woman who tries to do her best in raising Tom, is often annoyed with him, but loves him. 3-Tom's half-brother and half-sister 4-He knows what she is getting at, so makes an excuse about why his head and shirt might be wet.

Chapter 2: 1-He has to whitewash the fence for playing hooky and getting messed up fighting the new boy. 2-He doesn't like to see her cry; he loves her. 3-a marble; Aunt Polly spanks Jim with her slipper when she finds him giving up his pail to Tom. 4-He convinces other boys to pay him for the honor of painting the fence.

Chapter 3: 1-They pretend to be generals of opposing armies, while their "armies" of younger boys fight. 2-Amy has been Tom's girlfriend but now he is in love with the new girl, Becky Thatcher. 3-Sid breaks the sugar bowl, but Aunt Polly hits Tom, thinking he did it; she feels guilty, but worries that it will undermine her authority if she admits it. 4-He is melodramatic, and enjoys picturing how guilty his aunt would feel, after wrongly punishing him.

Chapter 4: 1-He has trouble; his mind wanders. 2-She gives him a Barlow knife for memorizing part of the Sermon on the Mount. 3-The tickets are given for memorizing Bible verses and are used to earn a Bible; Tom wants the glory of winning the Bible. 4-After claiming to have earned the Bible, but really trading for tickets, he can't say who the first two disciples are.

Chapter 5: 1-He traps a fly, then lets his pinch-bug loose. 2-A dog plays with it, yelps when he sits on it, and runs off with it.

Chapter 6: 1-He complains of his "mortified toe"—and his toothache. 2-After Aunt Polly pulls his tooth, he can spit in a new way. 3-Huck is the son of the town drunkard; the mothers don't like him because they think he is a poor role model for their sons. 4-They plan to go to the cemetery at midnight, wait until some devils come for the wicked man who has just died, then throw a dead cat at the devils, and say a chant. 5-He figures that he will have to sit with the girls as punishment—and he wants to be near Becky. 6-He writes "I love you" on a slate, gives her a peach.

Chapter 7: 1-a circus clown; 2-He mentions that he was engaged to another girl once. 3-the brass knob from an andiron; She hurls it down angrily.

Chapter 8: 1- a pirate 2-He believes that if you bury a marble for two weeks and say an incantation, all the marbles you've lost will end up in the box. 3-The next morning he will run away to be a pirate; he begins to collect his resources—starting with his marbles.

Chapter 9: 1-Huck comes to Tom's house and they go to the graveyard to cure warts. 2-They see Injun Joe, Muff Potter and Doc Robinson dig up a body. 3-Injun Joe demands more money from Doc. 4-Injun Joe kills Doc with Muff Potter's knife when Doc resists; Muff is drunk and Doc Robinson has knocked him out with a gravestone, so he believes Injun Joe's explanation that he (Muff) did it.

Chapter 10: 1-They wish to die if they ever tell what they have seen of the murder; they are afraid of Injun Joe. 2-Muff Potter 3-They think that the howling of a stray dog is a bad omen. 4-Sid tells on Tom. 5-for playing hooky 6-He remembers that he tried to give the knob to Becky and she rejected it.

Chapter 11: 1-His knife was found by the body. 2-for his knife 3-They have made a pact because they are afraid of Injun Joe—whose calculated lying makes him appear all the more a demon. 4-He has been having nightmares about the murder and needs an excuse to bandage his jaw to muffle anything he might say in his sleep. 5-He feels guilty and sorry for Muff, so brings him "small comforts."

Chapter 12: 1-He worries that she is sick and might die and he gets despondent. 2-trying out different remedies 3-He goes wild when Tom gives him some Pain-Killer. 4-Yes; he tries to get her attention and she says that he is showing off.

Chapter 13: 1-Becky is still angry with him, and he wants to make her and others who have "forsaken him" sorry. 2-His mother punished him for drinking cream he knew nothing about. 3-a ham, a side of bacon, a skillet, some tobacco and corn cobs to make pipes, a chunk of smoldering wood for fire, a raft 4-an island three miles below St. Petersburg; on the raft they stole; 5-stealing the meat

Chapter 14: 1-cooking over the fire, fishing, exploring; 2-to raise their bodies from the river, if they have drowned; 3-all three boys 4-We don't know yet; maybe he is "leaving them" to the boys in case he doesn't return.

Chapter 15: 1-wades, swims, hitches a ride on a skiff; He misses his aunt and wants to let her know that he is okay. 2-He hears Aunt Polly and Joe Harper's mother talking about how they miss the boys and regret punishing them. 3-kisses her 4-rows a skiff upstream; happy to see him; Joe was convinced all along he wouldn't disgrace himself as a pirate by failing to return.

Chapter 16: 1-hunt for turtle eggs, swim, play marbles, smoking; 2-tells them a secret; 3-smoke a pipe; 4-They both disappear to be sick from the smoking, but neither wants to admit it. 5-The tree that had sheltered their beds was blasted by lightning. 6-After playing Indians from hostile tribes, they have to make peace before they can eat supper together; they are glad to find that smoking no longer makes them sick.

Chapter 17: 1-All are upset, quiet, talk about their memories of the boys; they assume the boys have drowned after the raft is found. 2-The church is full; the clergyman praises the boys. 3-As the clergyman is crying and the mourners sobbing, the boys step out of the gallery; they are hugged and later cuffed.

Chapter 18: 1-He tells her about his "dream"—and describes what he saw when he sneaked home from the island and found Aunt Polly talking with Joe Harper's mother. 2-as a hero; 3-Becky spends time looking at a book with Alfred and Tom spends time head to head with Amy; yes, both are jealous. 4-After Becky tells him she hates him, Alfred realizes he has been "used" to make Tom jealous; he spills ink on Tom's spelling book.

Chapter 19: 1-Joe told Sereny that Tom sneaked home; Aunt Polly feels ridiculous for telling Sereny that Tom had a mystical dream. 2-She finds that he has been telling the truth; he did write her a note to tell her that he wasn't dead and the piece of bark on which it is written is in his pocket.

Chapter 20: 1-The teacher thinks he spilled the ink on his own book; Becky knew the truth. 2-She accidentally rips his book, but avoids punishment when Tom takes the blame. 3-No; Becky tells Tom that he is noble. 4-Becky tells Tom that Alfred spilled the ink on Tom's book.

Chapter 21: 1-He wants his students to put up a good show for Examination Day. 2-The teacher lives with his family and has "given the boy ample cause to hate him." 3-recitations—*Mary Had a Little Lamb, The Boy Stood on the Burning Deck,* reading exercises, a spelling fight, Latin recitation, original compositions; 4-While the teacher is drunk, the painter's son gilds his head; on Examination Day, a cat is lowered on a pulley; the cat grabs the teacher's toupée and all laugh.

Chapter 22: 1-Tom had just quit the Cadets, who now get to parade at the old man's funeral. 2-high points: minstrel shows, visits by a phrenologist and mesmerizer, the circus; 3-low points: He doesn't enjoy writing in his diary; rain on the 4th of July, no parade, a U.S. Senator is a disappointment; measles; 4-The revival has worn off; instead of studying the Bible, they are now eating a stolen melon.

Chapter 23: 1-The jury would give their verdict the following day. We later realize he was out seeing Muff's lawyer. 2- He knows he will be calling Tom to the stand, and that his testimony is Muff's only chance. 3-Tom tells about seeing Injun Joe kill the doctor. 4-He jumps out the window and runs away.

Chapter 24: 1-He is afraid that Injun Joe will get him. 2-Tom broke the pact of secrecy.

Chapter 25: 1-They hope to find buried treasure 2-Huck will have a pie and soda every day and go often to the circus; Tom will buy a new drum, sword, red necktie and a puppy, and get married. 3-in the haunted house

Chapter 26: 1-They think Friday is bad luck; they play Robin Hood instead. 2-The "Spaniard"—Injun Joe, and his unkempt partner in crime. 3-They are planning to do a "dangerous job," then go to Texas. 4-He is burying $650 in silver from previous robberies; a box full of gold buried by the Murrel gang. 5-They find the boys' pick and shovel. The stair breaks.

Chapter 27: 1-He and Huck overheard Injun Joe talk about taking the silver to "#2" and they think this might mean a room in the tavern. Tom finds that Room #2 in one of the taverns is a mystery even to the tavern-keeper. It's always kept locked, and they never see anyone go in or out. 2-They are both going to try every key they can find in the lock.

Chapter 28: 1-in an empty sugar hogshead (barrel); 2-liquor; "temperance" refers to abstinence, no liquor. 3-Huck will watch the tavern and go "meow" for Tom once he sees that Injun Joe has left; then they will both go in after the box.

Chapter 29: 1-They prepare a picnic and charter a steam-boat for her friends. 2-Instead of staying with Susy Harper, Becky accepts Tom's suggestion that they stop at Widow Douglas's. 3-Huck overhears Injun Joe say that he plans to cut the Widow Douglas because her late husband, the judge, had him horsewhipped for being a vagrant. 4-She has been kind to him; he goes to the Welshman and his three grown sons.

Chapter 30: 1-Huck is still afraid of Injun Joe and is afraid to reveal his disguise; he also does not want to reveal the treasure; the Welshman is suspicious about how the "deaf and dumb" Spaniard could talk about revenge against the widow. 2-Huck made him promise not to tell. 3-They don't worry until the next morning at church, when they realize the children have not been sleeping over at friends' houses. 4-Huck gets sick and the Welshman and doctors are off looking for Tom and Becky in the caves.

Chapter 31: 1-It is their last candle and he wants to save it. 2-Without light, they need to stay near a source of water. 3-some "wedding cake" from the picnic; 4-to keep busy; He ties kite-string to a projection and unwinds it as he goes. 5-Tom sees Injun Joe's hand holding a candle; Injun Joe runs.

Chapter 32: 1-Tom notices a speck of daylight and follows it to a small hole through which he and Becky push their way out. 2-Huck is still sick and Tom has been warned not to talk about anything too exciting. 3-He is drowned, probably while trying to escape. 4-Tom knows that Injun Joe is locked inside.

Chapter 33: 1-starvation; He had eaten candles and bats, tried to chip through the door with his knife, collected precious drops of water in a hollowed stone. 2-"Injun Joe's cup" 3-a petition to pardon Injun Joe; The narrator obviously believes that murderers should be punished, and that those who would pardon them are "weaklings." 4-He figures out that Injun Joe's den was in the cave, since that is where he last saw him. 5-Tom knows a secret entrance. 6-Huck thinks Injun Joe's ghost may haunt the place; Tom points out the cross in the cave and says that ghosts don't hang around where there are crosses. 7-They "borrow" Benny Taylor's wagon. 8-Most of the village's adults—the Thatchers, Harpers, Rogerses, Aunt Polly, etc. are there, waiting for them so that they can get on with a party to honor the Welshman and his sons for protecting the widow.

Chapter 34: 1-Huck wants to escape out a window because he isn't used to dressing up and being in a crowd. 2-Sid told the Welshman's "secret" about how Huck alerted him to Injun Joe's plans to harm the widow. 3-She intends to house him, have him educated, start him in a business; Huck is probably flattered, but somewhat unhappy with the idea of losing his freedom. 4-Tom brings in the money sacks; over $12,000.

Chapter 35: 1-Yes; the Widow Douglas oversees Huck's and Judge Thatcher oversees Tom's; each boy gets a dollar for every weekday and every other Sunday. 2-When the Judge hears Tom admit how he lied to protect Becky at school, the Judge compares the act to Washington's courageous admission that he had chopped down his father's cherry tree. 3-The Judge wants him to become a great lawyer or soldier, to go to the National Military Academy and later to the best law school; Tom probably has his doubts. 4-He is miserable having to be neat and clean and mannerly. 5-He tells Huck that Huck can join Tom's robber gang—but only if Huck is "respectable" and returns to the widow. 6-varied answers

Activities

Activities #1 and #2: Allow students time to discuss these and other open-ended activities (for which there are no "right" or "wrong" answers).

Activity #3: 1-ambuscade; 2-guileful; 3-skylarking; 4-glowering; 5-mien; 6-edifice; 7-disconcerted; 8-prodigy; 9-aides-de-campe; 10-alacrity; 11-15 will vary

Activity #4: maps will vary; All words should be mapped and maps shared.

Activity #5: 1-dejected; 2-serene; 3-compact; 4-remorse; 5-havoc; 6-fetters; 7-impudence; 8-persecuted; 9-dauntless; 10-miscreant; 11-16 will vary.

Activity #6: 1-repentant; 2-assent; 3-charily; 4-credulous; 5-abashed; 6-jubilant; 7-swarthy; 8-vindictive; 9-artlessly; 10-sumptuous; 11-fruitless; 12-sham

Activity #7: 1-diffident; 2-fickle; 3-gesticulation; 4-counsel; 5-sepulchral; 6-edification; 7-convalescent; 8-pate; 9-phrenologist; 10-omniscient

Activity #8: 1-labyrinth; 2-vagabond; 3-blanched

Activity #9:

  1.-antonyms: apathy-enthusiasm; synonyms: windfall-serendipity
  2.-antonyms: conspicuous-subtle; synonyms: benevolent-magnanimous
  3.-antonyms: gratification-displeasure; synonyms: moiety-half
  4.-antonyms: projection-recess; synonyms: shackle-bond
  5.-antonyms: dissented-agreed; synonyms: whetted-sharpened
  6.-antonyms: insipid-exciting; synonyms: crimson-red
  7.-antonyms: laudation-criticism; synonyms: avocation-profession
  8.-antonyms: unavailing-effective; synonyms: sinuous-meandering
  9.-antonyms: huzzas-boos; synonyms: provisions-supplies
 10.-antonyms: lethargy-animation; synonyms: pitfall-snare

Activity #10: The report card should reflect Tom's tendency to skip school and to daydream, his fairly good spelling ability, but his failure to "apply himself."

Activity #11: Student opinions will vary. The novel stands as a good example of how Afro-Americans and Native Americans were regarded in the mid-1800s; discussing the strides made—and not made— since then may be a helpful way to look at this aspect of the book.

Activity #12: Charts and essays will differ, but should reflect the fact that Tom prefers to use his time amusing himself rather than studying or working.

Activity #13: <u>Sample pros</u>: It is the right thing to do; it will keep an innocent man from being punished. <u>Sample cons</u>: Injun Joe might seek vengeance against the boys; Aunt Polly might punish Tom for holding back for so long.

Activity #14: [Student-created similes (part c) will vary.]
    1.   a) the new boy and Tom, fighting cats
          b) Both grip each other and fight wildly.
    2.   a) the thought of missing out on fun, fire
          b) Both are painful, burning.
    3.   a) the clods of earth and hailstones
          b) Both are hard pellets that are hurled.
    4.   a) the river and the ocean when it is calm
          b) Both are smooth, vast bodies of water.
    5.   a) anxiety and a mountain
          b) Both are massive.

Activity #15: Video reviews will vary.

Activity #16: I. Diction: Answers will vary, but both rewrites should still reflect how melodramatic Tom is—the exaggerated sense of desolation as he thinks of drowning himself.

II. Dialect: Answers will vary: A.Samples—'twas for it was; wisht for wished; afeard for afraid; foller for follow   B.Samples—"deed and double deed" for dare and double dare; "kept mum" for "kept quiet"; "by jingoes" for "mark my words" or "I swear" C. 1. Older people are set in their ways. 2-I get mad. 3-He's a spunky troublemaker. 4-You have to punish kids or they get spoiled. 5-12 vary.

Activity #17: Essays will vary.

Activity #18: Crossword key on next page.

Quizzes and Tests

Comprehension Quiz (correcting true-false): 1-F; because he didn't like boy's citified look; 2-F; She often let him get by without punishment and he knew that and loved her. 3-F; to paint the fence as punishment for playing hooky; 4-F; They paid him these items for the privilege. 5-T; 6-T; 7-T; 8-F; He

---

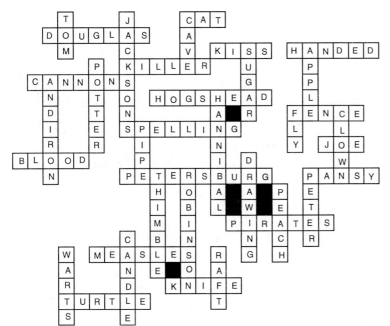

traded his treasures for tickets to earn the Bible. 9-T; 10-F; His aunt pulled the tooth and his spitting ability happened to improve. 11-F; Most disliked him because they considered him vulgar and a poor influence on their children. 12-F-to cure warts; 13-T; 14-T; 15-F; because he mentioned an old girlfriend; 16-T; 17-F; Injun Joe was the murderer. 18-T; 19-T; 20-F; She loved trying new remedies.

Comprehension Quiz (completion) (Accept other answers that are the equivalent of these):1-played hooky; 2-whitewash; 3-convincing other boys to pay him to let them do it; 4-tickets; 5-memorizing Bible verses; 6-Bible; 7-disciples; 8-pulling his tooth; 9-cat; 10-warts; 11-devil; 12-wicked; 13-graveyard; 14-midnight; 15-with the girls near Becky; 16-Becky Thatcher; 17-drawings; 18- I love you; 19-Amy Lawrence; 20-andiron knob; 21-Huck; 22-Muff Potter, Injun Joe; 23-Injun Joe; 24-Doc Robinson; 25-tell anyone that they had seen the murder; 26-Muff Potter; 27-Becky Thatcher; 28-running away from home; 29-Huck Finn; 30-Joe Harper

Novel Test I

Identification: 1-D, 2-B, 3-H, 4-C, 5-G, 6-K, 7-A, 8-M, 9-L, 10-I, 11-E, 12-J, 13-F

Multiple Choice: 1-(1); 2-(4); 3-(3); 4-(2); 5-(4); 6-(2); 7-(1); 8-(3); 9-(2); 10-(1); 11-(3); 12-(4); 13-(3); 14-(4); 15-(1); 16-(3); 17-(1); 18-(2); 19-(3); 20-(4); 21-(2); 22-(3); 23-(3); 24-(4); 25-(2)

Essay Section: A.Sample—The student might describe how the boys steal a raft and camp on the island, where they pretend to be pirates. B.The student answer should refer to the boys' fear of Injun Joe—and Tom's sense of guilt over letting Muff Potter go to a trial for a crime he didn't commit. C.The "diary entry" should explain how Becky was snooping in the teacher's book, ripped it, let Tom "take the rap"—and how honorable Becky thought Tom was. D. Aunt Polly and Mary would probably show how much they missed Tom, although Aunt Polly might rebuke him; Sid would get in his "digs" as his jealousy showed through.

Novel Test II

Identification: A.Aunt Polly-Tom's guardian, his dead mother's sister, She is religious, tries to discipline Tom, has a lot of affection for him. B.Tom Sawyer-the 10-year-old main character, adventure-loving, rule-breaking; C.Huck Finn-the son of the town drunkard, a good friend of Tom's who lives on his own, envied by the other children; D. Joe Harper-friend of Tom's who pretends with Tom that they are generals waging battle on the town square; E. Injun Joe-criminal who kills Doc Robinson; F. Doc Robinson-young doctor who is murdered while trying to steal a recently buried body; G. Muff Potter-a town drunk who agrees to help unearth the body and is charged with Doc Robinson's murder; H.Sid-Tom's half-brother, always snitching on Tom; I.Mary-Tom's mature, religious, kind, older half-sister; J. Becky Thatcher-the new girl, daughter of Judge Thatcher, on whom Tom has a crush; K. Alfred Temple-the "citified" new boy Tom can't stand, used by Becky to make Tom jealous; L. Widow Douglas-widow of a judge who had Injun Joe horsewhipped, she wants to adopt Huck Finn.

Short Answer

The answers should refer to these details:

1- Sid pointed out that Tom's collar was sewn with a different color thread from the one Aunt Polly had used, so he must have removed the collar to go swimming.
2- They loved each other; he tried to get around her rules and she tried her best to be a good "parent."
3- He convinced the other boys that it was fun, and they paid him for the "privilege" of painting the fence.
4- Tom traded the things he had gotten in the fence fiasco for tickets he could use to get a Bible.
5- Huck told Tom that this was a necessary step in a ritual for removing warts.
6- They saw three men unearth a body, then one—Injun Joe— killed the second—Doc Robinson—and told the third—Muff Potter—that Muff had done it.
7- He mentioned an old girlfriend, Amy.
8- The boys felt misunderstood, so stole a raft and camped on a nearby island.
9- They returned in the middle of their own funeral service.
10-He seemed lethargic; he tormented the cat by giving it a dose and pointed out that his aunt was similarly tormenting him.
11-Samples: Aunt Polly punished him for breaking the sugar bowl and the teacher punished him for spilling ink on his spelling book.
12-He "admitted" ripping the teacher's book.
13-Resentful of how hard he had been driving them, the children had one boy gild the teacher's head while he was drunk. Later, in front of students and families, the teacher lost his wig to the claws of a cat lowered from overhead by a student.
14-They had disappeared in the cave.
15-They discovered the treasure in the cave (gold that was buried by Injun Joe, originally stolen by a gang of thieves).
16-His knife was found by the body and Injun Joe said that Potter committed the murder.
17-Tom told Potter's lawyer the truth and Injun Joe escaped while Tom was on the stand.
18-The doctor drove him away from his father's kitchen and his father had him jailed as a vagrant; the widow's husband, a judge, had Injun Joe horsewhipped for vagrancy.
19-He was accidentally locked in the cave, without food.
20-Huck didn't like having to wear neat clothes, eat politely, etc. Tom convinced him that in order to join Tom's group of robbers, Huck must learn to be "respectable."

Written Response

A. Sample—Twain pokes fun at the "weaklings" who formed a committee and petitioned for Injun Joe's pardon. Twain is criticizing what he sees as a misguided tendendcy to want to pity/reform "hardened" criminals, rather than punish them.

B. Samples: 1-The boys run away from home and camp on an island. 2-Tom gets into trouble at school for breaking the rules by doing such things as playing with ticks and arriving late to class; Huck doesn't go to school at all. 3-Rather than tell adults what they know about the "Spaniard" and his thieving partner, the boys spy on these two and find their hidden treasure.

C. Students should mention that critics have objected to the portrayal of blacks and Native Americans; defenders suggest that the book is a model of good writing to which students should be exposed and that the portrayals of minorities reflect attitudes of Twain's time that should be discussed, not ignored.

D? The monologue should reflect Tom's anxiety, his decision-making process (as he weighs pros and cons—his fear of Injun Joe, his desire to do what is ethically right), his concern about breaking a promise to Huck.